Maths Sticker Work[book]
Addition

Wendy Clemson and David Clemson

Note to parents

This book is part of a programme of workbook titles that are designed to support school-work and make learning fun. It covers all the main addition concepts that your child will need to know as a young learner of maths: how to add to 100, use a number line, estimate, recognize odds and evens, understand tens and units, and solve complex sums.

Many of the maths questions and puzzles in **Addition** are answered with stickers, which are found on the middle two pages of the book. Answers to all the questions appear on page 16.

The following symbols are used in this book:

The star symbol means there is a sticker to put here on the page.

Wherever your child needs to fill in an answer, there is a blue box like this one to write in.

There is a space for working out answers on each page, indicated by this pencil symbol.

In the top left-hand corner of each page there is a space for a "reward" sticker. Add it once your child has completed the puzzles.

DK

DORLING KINDERSLEY
London • New York • Stuttgart • Moscow

Sums in disguise

Join these children at the fancy dress party to help you learn how to add up different numbers of things.

Adding

Addition is putting together numbers to make a total. Additions are called sums. Sum is another word for total.

2 children   add   1 more child   makes   3 children in total

$$2 + 1 = 3$$

Symbol for two   Add sign   Symbol for one   Makes or equals   Total

You write the sum this way using signs and symbols.

Dressing up

Here are some children at a fancy dress party.

Work across the page, adding as you go. Put the sticker of one more fire-fighter below, then do the sum.

$$4 + \boxed{} = \boxed{}$$

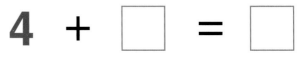

Party hats

Draw two hats in the space for each sum below and then fill in the answers.

□ + □ = □

1 + □ + □ = □

2 + □ + 2 = □

Animal masks

Here are three animal masks. Draw four more masks in the space. Can you work out the sum?

□ + □ = □

Find the sticker showing two more children and complete the sum.

5 + □ = □

☆

Here are three more children in fancy dress. How many children are there altogether at the party?

□
Total children

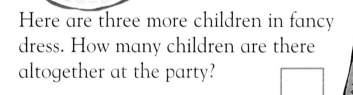

Jungle number trails

Here are some jungle problems for you to solve. Use the number line below to help you.

Perching parrots

Here are six parrots perched on a branch.

$6 + 1 = \boxed{}$

$7 + 1 = \boxed{}$

$8 + 1 = \boxed{}$

More parrots are arriving to join them. Can you add the parrots, one at a time?

$9 + 1 = \boxed{}$

Number line

Count along the number line to help you add up. To add seven to five, put your finger on the five and move on seven spaces. What is the answer? $\boxed{}$

| 1 | 2 | 3 | 4 | 5 | 6 | 7 | 8 | 9 | 10 | 11 | 12 | 13 | 14 | 15 | 16 | 17 | 18 | 19 | 20 |

Add six leopards and seven toucans. What is the total number of creatures? $\boxed{}$

Now add eleven cobras and eight orang-utans. $\boxed{}$

Adding adders!

How many snakes are slithering across the jungle floor? ☐

Starting with this number, work out these additions.

☐ + **3** = ☐

☐ + **10** = ☐

☐ + **9** = ☐

Brilliant butterflies

Find the stickers of four butterflies. If you add seven more, what is the total?

Circle the right answer. **10** **11** **12**

Using this total, how many more butterflies need to flutter around the flower to give a total of 17? ☐

Leap frogs

Follow the frogs through this long sum and add the numbers as you go. What is the final total?

1 + 5 + 3 + 1 + 4 + 1 + 3 + 2 = ☐

Tasty additions

Practise your adding with these delicious cake and pizza puzzles, and see if you can crack the tricky fruit code.

Decorate a cake

Draw two chocolate drops in the spaces in the sums below and work out the answers.

$2 +$ 🍫🍫 $=$ 4

$6 +$ ☐ $=$ ☐

$9 +$ ☐ $=$ ☐

What number needs to be added to the numbers of sweets below?

🍬🍬🍬🍬🍬🍬 $+$ ☐ $= 11$

🍬 $+$ ☐ $= 7$

🍬🍬🍬 $+$ ☐ $= 9$

Add 10 candles each time in these sums.

$8 +$ 🕯🕯🕯🕯🕯🕯🕯🕯🕯🕯 $=$ ☐

$4 +$ 🕯🕯🕯🕯🕯🕯🕯🕯🕯🕯 $=$ ☐

$9 +$ 🕯🕯🕯🕯🕯🕯🕯🕯🕯🕯 $=$ ☐

Add seven cherries each time. Can you work out the numbers that start these sums?

☐ $+$ 🍒🍒🍒🍒🍒🍒🍒 $= 12$

☐ $+$ 🍒🍒🍒🍒🍒🍒🍒 $= 8$

☐ $+$ 🍒🍒🍒🍒🍒🍒🍒 $= 14$

How many biscuits?

Estimate how many biscuits you think are in this pile in total.

Circle the closest answer.   **10**   **15**   **20**

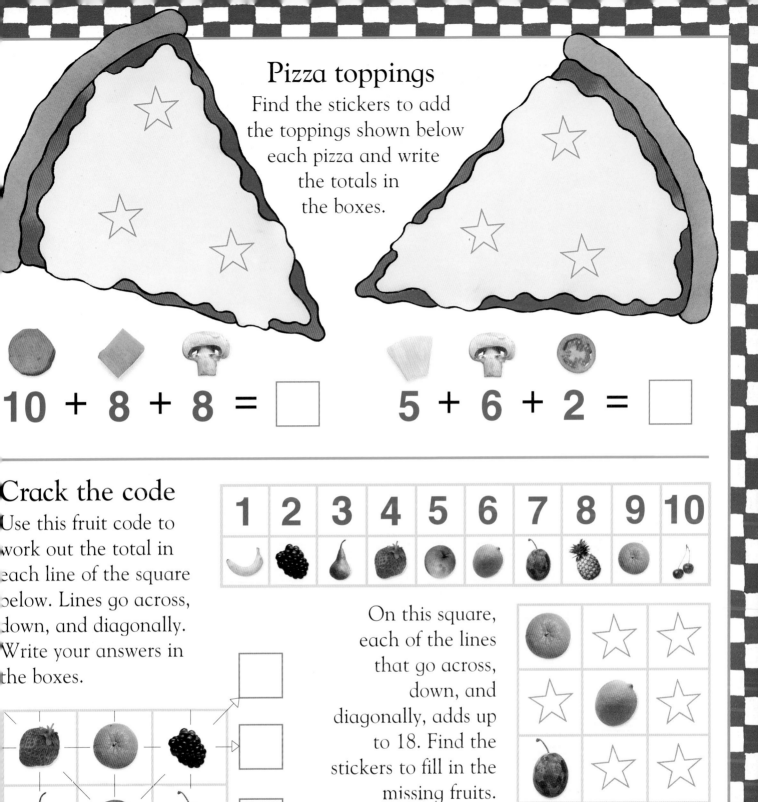

Pizza toppings

Find the stickers to add the toppings shown below each pizza and write the totals in the boxes.

10 + 8 + 8 = ☐

5 + 6 + 2 = ☐

Crack the code

Use this fruit code to work out the total in each line of the square below. Lines go across, down, and diagonally. Write your answers in the boxes.

1	2	3	4	5	6	7	8	9	10

On this square, each of the lines that go across, down, and diagonally, adds up to 18. Find the stickers to fill in the missing fruits.

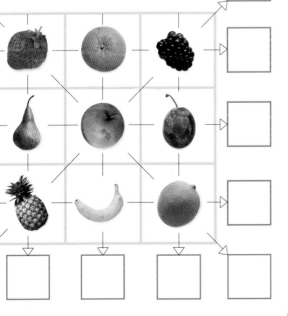

Odds and evens

This number line has seagulls on the odd numbers. All the other numbers on the number line are even.

1 2 3 4 5 6 7 8 9 10 11 12 13 14 15 16 17 18 19 20

Sea creatures puzzle

Look at the sums below. The answers are either an odd or even number. Can you add the sea creatures and find the sticker answers?

+ = **even**

+ = ☆

+ = ☆

+ = ☆

+ = ☆

Dot-to-dot

If you join the odd numbered dots, what do you see?

Pages 2/3
Sums in disguise
Dressing up

Pages 4/5 Jungle number trails
Brilliant butterflies

Pages 6/7 Tasty additions
Crack the code

Pizza toppings

Reward stickers
When a page is completed
and the answers checked,
reward yourself with the
right sticker.

Page 8 Odds and evens
Sea creatures puzzle

Page 9 Number puzzles
Sandy sums

Pages 12/13 Missing numbers
Number sequences

Page 10/11 Going up!
Setting out sums

51	34	70
18	15	28

Space travel

48 days   90 days

39 days   80 days

Pages 14/15
Airshow game

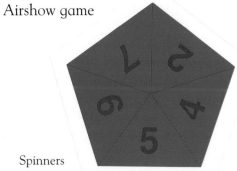 

Spinners

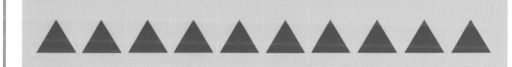

Game counters

Number puzzles

Here are some seaside sums. Can you work out the answers?

Sandy sums

Which numbers when added to themselves several times make the number 12? Put the flag stickers on the right sandcastles.

Catch a fish

These fishermen have caught fish with sums on them. What number do they add up to?

Hidden colours

What is lurking in this picture? Work out the sums below to crack the colour code and colour in the picture.

9 = red **10** = blue **11** = yellow **12** = green

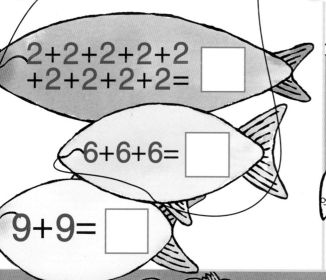

2+2+2+2+2
+2+2+2+2= ☐

6+6+6= ☐

9+9= ☐

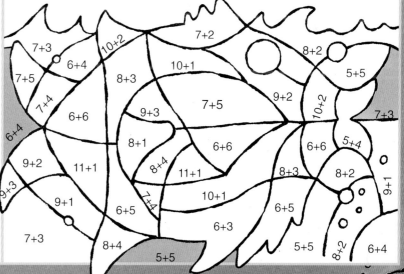

Going up!

Try these space age sums and learn how to add up big numbers.

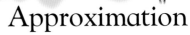

5 44 26 9 37 11 16 32 40 3

Tens and units

Look at the number ten.

This number shows us there is 1 ten.

10

This number shows us there are 0 ones or units.

15 Fifteen is **1** ten and **5** units.

26 Twenty six is **2** tens and **6** units.

Tick the numbers below that have 4 tens.

41 ☐ **64** ☐ **49** ☐ **14** ☐

Which of these numbers have 2 units?

12 ☐ **22** ☐ **20** ☐ **92** ☐

Here is another way of showing tens and units.

Tens

Units

32

 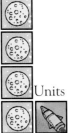 

Tens

Units

Tens

Units

_____ _____

Can you write in the missing numbers that match these tens and units?

Approximation

If you know roughly what your answer will be, it helps you check your calculation.

37 + 4 is approximately **40**

60 + 22 is approximately **80**

Write down approximate answers to these additions.

72 + 17 is approximately ☐

14 + 24 is approximately ☐

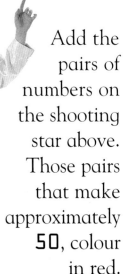

Add the pairs of numbers on the shooting star above. Those pairs that make approximately **50**, colour in red.

Setting out sums

We can write a sum in two different ways.

$$23 + 11 = 34$$

$$
\begin{array}{r}
23 \\
+ \ 11 \\
\hline
34
\end{array}
$$

This sum puts the tens and units in the right place to help you add up.

Find the sticker sums that give these answers.

☆ + ☆ + ☆

69   **49**   **98**

Rocket timing

| 72 hours standby | 24 hours countdown |

How long is standby and countdown time altogether?

[ ] hours

If standby time is 52 hours and countdown 12 hours how many hours is that in total?

[ ] hours

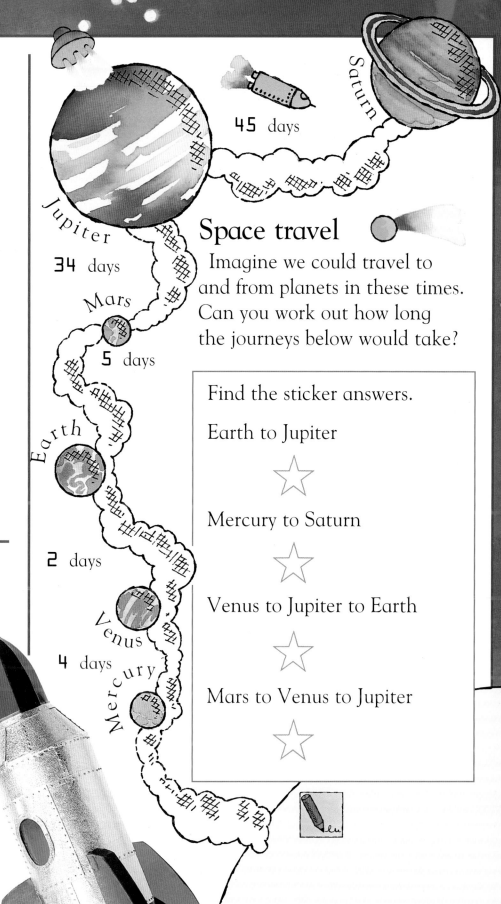

Saturn
45 days

Jupiter
34 days

Mars
5 days

Earth

2 days

Venus
4 days

Mercury

Space travel

Imagine we could travel to and from planets in these times. Can you work out how long the journeys below would take?

Find the sticker answers.

Earth to Jupiter

☆

Mercury to Saturn

☆

Venus to Jupiter to Earth

☆

Mars to Venus to Jupiter

☆

Missing numbers

See if you can work out the missing numbers in these spooky sequences.

Number sequences

Add two to the number on each pumpkin to get the next number in the sequence.

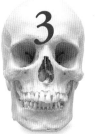   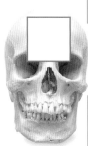

What is the number on the last skull?

Follow the witches' trail to work out the number on the last witch.

What number have you added each time?

5

5

11

23

18

+20

This spider adds 20 to every number it is given. Can you write in the answers?

Adding spiders

These creepy spiders love adding numbers. They add the same amount to any number given to them.

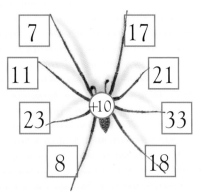

7   17
11   21
+10
23   33
8   18

This spider adds 10 to every number. Follow the pairs of legs to get the answers.

12

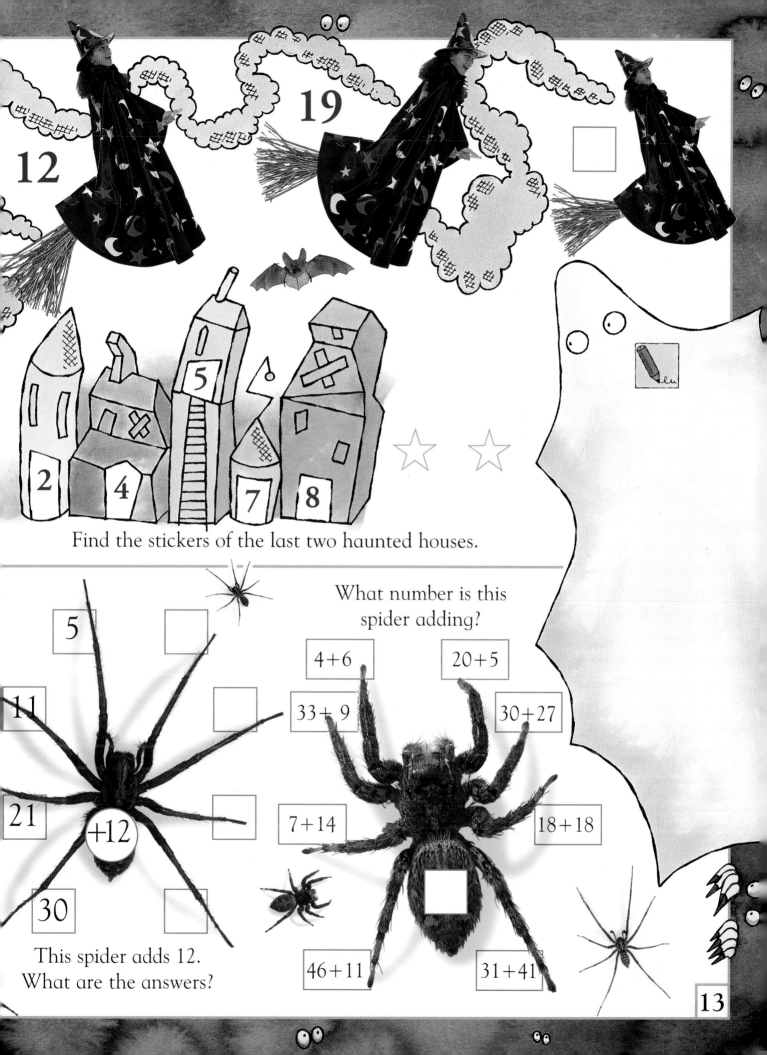

12

19

Find the stickers of the last two haunted houses.

5

11

21 (+12)

30

This spider adds 12.
What are the answers?

What number is this
spider adding?

4+6   20+5

33+9   30+27

7+14   18+18

46+11   31+41

13

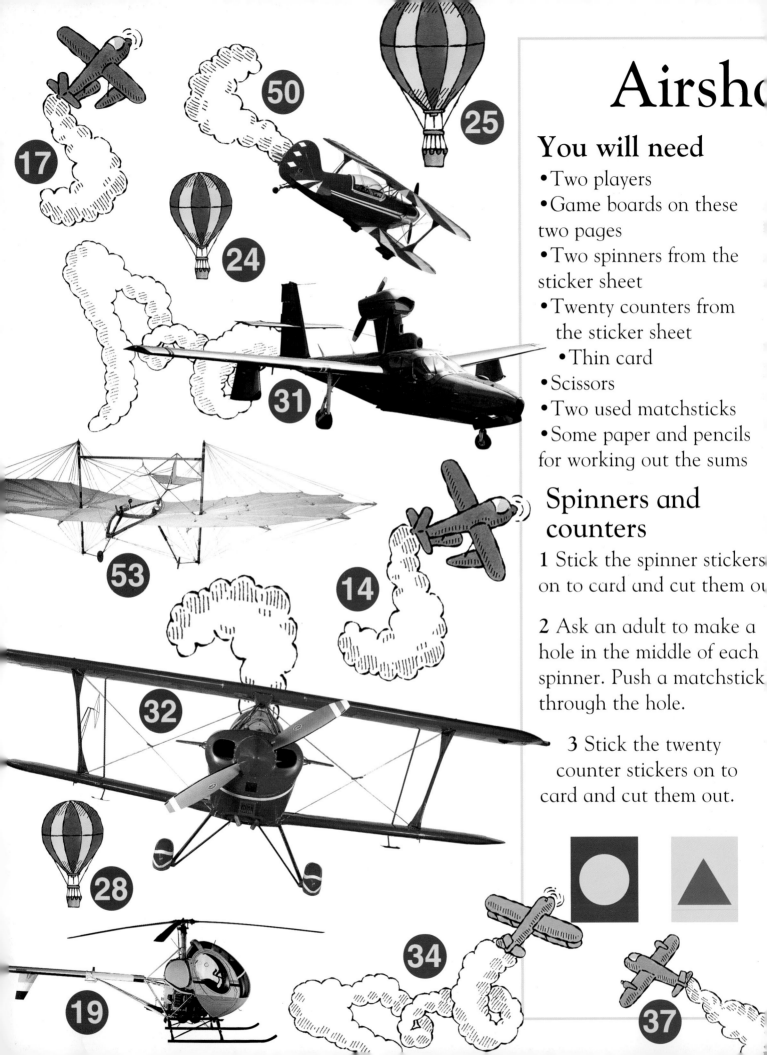

Airsho

You will need

- Two players
- Game boards on these two pages
- Two spinners from the sticker sheet
- Twenty counters from the sticker sheet
- Thin card
- Scissors
- Two used matchsticks
- Some paper and pencils for working out the sums

Spinners and counters

1 Stick the spinner stickers on to card and cut them ou

2 Ask an adult to make a hole in the middle of each spinner. Push a matchstick through the hole.

3 Stick the twenty counter stickers on to card and cut them out.

game

How to play

• Each player selects one of the two game boards and the matching set of counters.

• Players take it in turns to spin the two spinners. Look for the numbers on the sides of the spinners that rest on the table. Add together the two numbers to get a player's total. It may help to work out the sum on a piece of paper.

• If the total appears on the player's game board, he or she takes one of the counters and places it over the number. Then the player has another go.

• The winner is the first player to place all ten counters on the board.

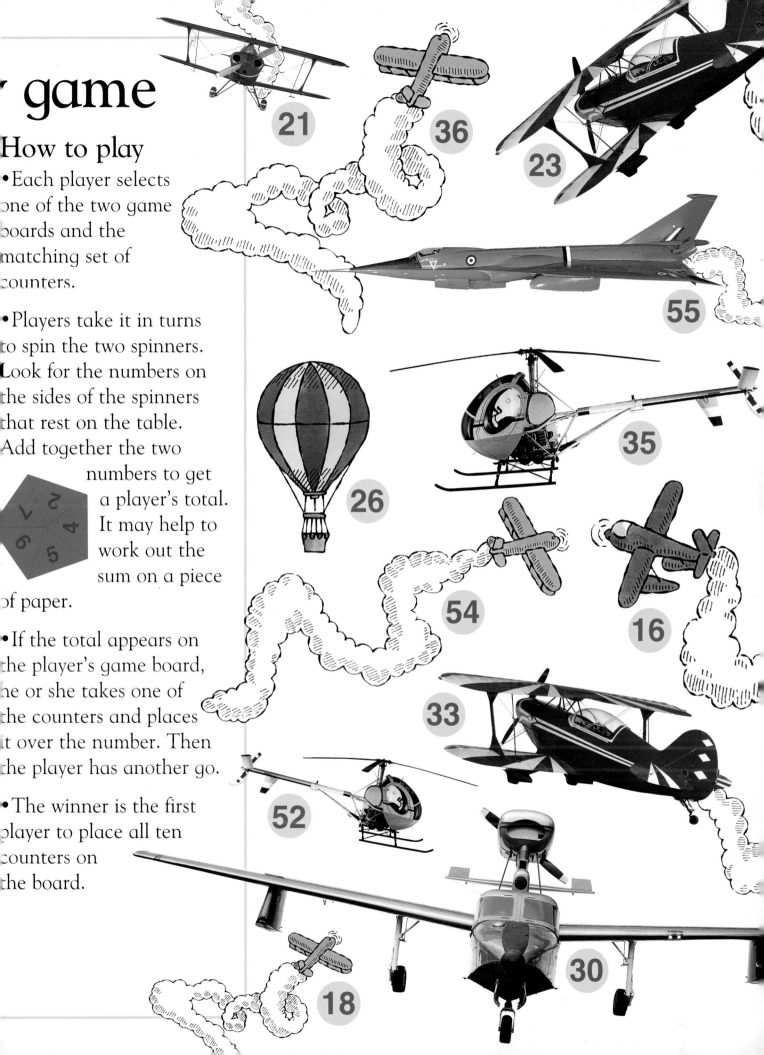

Answers

Pages 2/3 Sums in disguise
Dressing up
4+1=**5**
5+2=**7**
Total number of children: **10**

Party hats
2+2=**4**
1+2+2=**5**
2+2+2=**6**

Animal masks
3+4=**7**

Pages 4/5 Jungle number trails
Perching parrots
6+1=**7**
7+1=**8**
8+1=**9**
9+1=**10**

Number line
5+7= **12**
6 leopards +**7** toucans =**13**
11 cobras +**8** orang-utans =**19**

Adding adders!
8 snakes
8+3=**11**
8+10=**18**
8+9=**17**

Brilliant butterflies
4 butterflies +**7** more =**11**
11+**6** more butterflies =**17**

Leap frogs
1+5+3+1+4+1+3+2=**20**

Pages 6/7 Tasty additions
Decorate a cake

Chocolate drops	Sweets
2+2=**4**	5+6=**11**
6+2=**8**	1+6=**7**
9+2=**11**	3+6=**9**

Candles	Cherries
8+10=**18**	5+7=**12**
4+10=**14**	1+7=**8**
9+10=**19**	7+7=**14**

How many biscuits?
The total is closest to **10**.

Pizza toppings
10+8+8=**26**
5+6+2=**13**

Crack the code
The total for all lines is **15**.

Page 8 Odds and evens
Sea creatures puzzle
8+3=11 odd
2+4=6 even
3+1=4 even
6+7=13 odd

Dot-to-dot
A lighthouse.

Page 9 Number puzzles
Sandy sums
2+2+2+2+2+2=**12**
3+3+3+3=**12**
4+4+4=**12**
6+6=**12**

Catch a fish
2+2+2+2+2+2+2+2+2=**18**
6+6+6=**18**
9+9=**18**

Hidden colours

Pages 10/11 Going up!
Tens and units
These numbers have four tens:
4**1** 4**9**
These numbers have two units:
1**2** 2**2** 9**2**

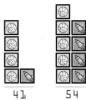

41   54

Approximation
7**2** + 1**7** is approximately **90**
1**4** + 2**4** is approximately **40**
These pairs on the shooting star are approximately **50**:
5+44, 37+11, 16+32

Setting out sums

51	34	70
+18	+15	+28
69	**49**	**98**

Rocket timing
72+24=**96** hours
52+12=**64** hours

Space travel
Earth to Jupiter takes: 5+34=**39** days
Mercury to Saturn takes: 4+2+5+34+45=**90** days
Venus to Jupiter to Earth takes: 2+5+34+34+5=**80** days
Mars to Venus to Jupiter takes: 5+2+2+5+34=**48** days

Pages 12/13 Missing numbers
Number sequences
The number on the last skull is **15**.
The number on the last witch is **26**. You have added **7** each time.
10 and **11** are the last two numbers on the haunted houses.

Adding spiders

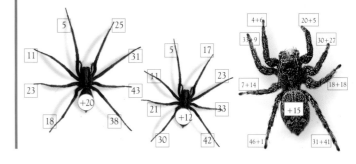

DK

A DORLING KINDERSLEY BOOK
Editor Victoria Edgley
Senior Editor Susan Peach
Designer Kate Eagar
Assistant Designer Caroline Potts
Managing Editor Jane Yorke
Managing Art Editor Chris Scollen
Production Ruth Cobb
Jacket Designer Mark Haygarth
Illustrations by Sally Kindberg
Photography by Philip Dowell, Geoff Dunn, Mike Dunning, Steve Gorton, Frank Greenaway, David Johnson, Colin Keates, Dave King, Cyril Laubscher, Susanna Price, Steve Shott, and Jerry Young

First published in Great Britain in 1997
by Dorling Kindersley Limited,
9 Henrietta Street,
London WC2E 8PS

A CIP catalogue record for this book is available from the British Library.

ISBN 0-7513-5566-6

Colour reproduction by Colourscan, Singapore
Printed and bound in Italy by Graphicom